Presenting the Past Teacher's Resources 2

Britain 1500–1750

Keith Worrall

Published by Collins Educational
An imprint of HarperCollins*Publishers* Limited
77–85 Fulham Palace Road
Hammersmith
London
W6 8JB

www.**Collins**Education.com
On-line support for schools and colleges

© HarperCollins*Publishers* Ltd 2002
First published 2002

ISBN 0 00 711460 5

Keith Worrall asserts his moral right to be identified as
the author of this work.

British Library Cataloguing in Publication Data.
A catalogue record for this publication is available from
the British Library.

Edited by Samantha Davey
Design by Ken Vail Graphic Design, Cambridge
Cover design by Derek Lee
Artwork by Peter Bull and Daniel Betts
Production by James Graves
Printed and bound by Martin's The Printers, Berwick upon Tweed

Acknowledgements

Every effort has been made to contact the holders of copyright material but if
any have been inadvertently overlooked the Publishers will be pleased to
make the necessary arrangements at the first opportunity.

Photographs
The Publishers would like to thank the following for permission to reproduce
photographs on these pages:

T = top, B = bottom, C = centre, L = left, R = right

Ashmolean Museum, Oxford 38; Mary Evans Picture Library 14TR; National
Museum, Stockholm, 14BL; National Portrait Gallery, London, 14TL, 14BR.

Cover image: BAL 72630 The Execution of Lady Jane Grey in the Tower of
London in 1553, 1833 by Hippolyte Delaroche (Paul) (1797–1856),
National Gallery, London, UK/Bridgeman Art Library

Realia
The Publishers would like to thank the following for references made to their
work in *Presenting the Past Book Two Britain 1500–1750: Teacher's Resources:*
Worksheet 2.10, C V Wedgwood, *The Trial of Charles I*, Weidenfeld &
Nicholson, 1964.

Contents

Introduction

The aim of the *Presenting the Past* series is to provide exciting and different approaches to teaching history at Key Stage 3, aimed at pupils of all abilities. Active learning is achieved through a range of teaching strategies, which relate to and support current national initiatives. These initiatives include the new National Strategy, the roll out of the National Literacy Strategy, and the introduction of Citizenship education as a National Curriculum subject. All of these impact upon the teaching of History at Key Stage 3 and it is the purpose of this series to support the teacher in delivering high quality teaching whilst, at the same time, taking on board the implications of these initiatives when planning schemes of work for Key Stage 3 History.

This teacher's guide identifies the links between *Presenting the Past Book Two* and the History Programme of Study, QCA Schemes of Work (2000), the National Literacy Framework, QCA Scheme of Work for Citizenship (2001), ICT activities and Key Skills.

In addition to the series of photocopiable support worksheets there are recommendations for further extension activities. These suggestions will support less-able pupils and stretch more-able pupils in line with DfES recommendations for Gifted and Talented Pupils at Key Stage 3. Relevant worksheets are listed in brackets next to the teacher's notes relating to each pupil book unit, for example (w1.9). Where provided, warm-up activities are intended to act as an introduction to new concepts and skills and should be undertaken prior to looking at the particular topic in the pupil book.

Guidance given within this book is purely recommendation and advice. There is plenty of scope here to develop a range of teaching and learning styles. You may wish to develop your own activities from these suggestions and use the resources as a starting point to develop ideas to match your scheme of work and assessment needs according to the ability of your pupils.

Authors

Tony McAleavy is the former Humanities Advisor for Gloucestershire County Council, and a leading member of the team that produced the QCA Scheme of Work.

Andrew Wrenn is the Humanities Advisor for Cambridgeshire County Council and an expert on the relationship between Citizenship and History.

Keith Worrall is the General Inspector for Humanities, PSHE and Citizenship for Doncaster.

Paul Grey is the General Inspector for Humanities, PSHE and Citizenship at the London Borough of Havering.

Rosemarie Little has been a successful History teacher for 13 years, an LEA advisory teacher for History and a freelance History consultant.

Opportunities for producing evidence of Citizenship and Literacy can be found in the matrices at the beginning of each section. The abbreviations in these sections of the matrices relate to the NC Programme of Study for KS3 Citizenship and QCA's *Framework for teaching English: Years 7, 8 and 9.*

◆ Citizenship

Knowledge and understanding about becoming informed citizens. Pupils should be taught about:

a the legal and human rights and responsibilities underpinning society, basic aspects of the criminal justice system, and how both relate to young people

b the diversity of national, regional, religious and ethnic identities in the United Kingdom and the need for mutual respect and understanding

c central and local government, the public services they offer and how they are financed, and the opportunities to contribute

d the key characteristics of parliamentary and other forms of government

e the electoral system and the importance of voting

f the work of community-based, national and international voluntary groups

g the importance of resolving conflict fairly

h the significance of the media in society

i the world as a global community, and the political, economic, environmental and social implications of this, and the role of the European Union, the Commonwealth and the United Nations.

◆ Literacy

NB: Opportunities for Vocabulary and Spelling are found throughout *Presenting the Past Book Two*

Teaching Objectives Year 7
Sentence level

8 recognise the cues to start a new paragraph and use the first sentence effectively to orientate the reader, e. g. *when there is a shift of topic, viewpoint or time;*

12 organise ideas into a coherent sequence of paragraphs, introducing, developing and concluding them appropriately;

Reading level

Pupils should be taught to:

1 know how to locate resources for a given task, and find relevant information in them, e. g. *skimming, use of index, glossary, key words, hotlinks;*

2 use appropriate reading strategies to extract particular information, e.g *highlighting, scanning;*

3 compare and contrast the ways information is presented in different forms, e.g. *web page, diagrams, prose;*

4 make brief, clearly-organised notes of key points for later use;

5 appraise the value and relevance of information found and acknowledge sources;

6 adopt active reading approaches to engage with and make sense of texts, e.g. *visualising, predicting, empathising and relating to own experience;*

7 identify the main points, processes or ideas in a text and how they are sequenced and developed by the writer;

8 infer and deduce meanings using evidence in the text, identifying where and how meanings are implied;

9 distinguish between the views of the writer and those expressed by others in the text, e.g. *the narrator, quoted experts, characters;*

10 identify how media texts are tailored to suit their audience, and recognise that audience responses vary, e.g. *popular websites;*

Writing level

Pupils should be taught to:

1 plan, draft, edit, revise, proofread and present a text with readers and purpose in mind;

2 collect, select and assemble ideas in a suitable planning format, e.g. *flow chart, list, star chart;*

3 use writing to explore and develop ideas, e.g. *journals, brainstorming techniques and mental mapping activities;*

5 structure a story with an arresting opening, a developing plot, a complication, a crisis and a satisfying resolution;

11 select and present information using detail, example, diagram and illustration as appropriate;

12 develop ideas and lines of thinking in continuous text and explain a process logically, highlighting the links between cause and effect;

14 describe an object, person or setting in a way that includes relevant details and is accurate and evocative;

15 express a personal view, adding persuasive emphasis to key points, e.g. *by reiteration, exaggeration, repetition, use of rhetorical questions;*

16 find and use different ways to validate an argument, e.g. statistical evidence, exemplification, testimony;

18 identify criteria for evaluating a particular situation, object or event, present findings fairly and give a personal view;

Speaking and Listening

Pupils should be taught to:

1 use talk as a tool for clarifying ideas, e.g. *by articulating problems or asking pertinent questions;*

2 recount a story, anecdote or experience, and consider how this differs from written narrative;

3 tailor the structure, vocabulary and delivery of a talk or presentation so that listeners can follow it;

10 identify and report the main points emerging from discussion, e.g. *to agree a course of action including responsibilities and deadlines;*

11 adopt a range of roles in discussion, including acting as spokesperson, and contribute in different ways such as promoting, opposing, exploring and questioning;

12 use exploratory, hypothetical and speculative talk as a way of researching ideas and expanding thinking;

13 work together logically and methodically to solve problems, make deductions, share, test and evaluate ideas;

14 acknowledge other people's views, justifying or modifying their own views in the light of what others say;

15 develop drama techniques to explore in role a variety of situations and texts or respond to stimuli;

17 extend their spoken repertoire by experimenting with language in different roles and dramatic contexts;

Teaching Objectives Year 8
Sentence level

1 combine clauses into complex sentences, using the comma effectively as a boundary signpost and checking for fluency and clarity, e. g. *using non-finite clauses;*

4 explore the effects of changes in tense, e. g. *past to present for vividness;*

5 recognise and exploit the use of conditionals and modal verbs when speculating, hypothesising or discussing possibilities;

6 explore and compare different methods of grouping sentences into paragraphs of continuous text that are clearly focused and well developed, e. g. *by chronology, comparison or through adding exemplification;*

7 develop different ways of linking paragraphs, using a range of strategies to improve cohesion and coherence, e. g. *choice of connectives, reference back, linking phrases;*

12 explore and use different degrees of formality in written and oral texts, e. g. formal speeches, informal journals;

13 recognise some of the differences in sentence structure, vocabulary and tone between a modern English text and a text from another historical period;

Reading level

1 combine information from various sources into one coherent document;

2 undertake independent research using a range of reading strategies, applying their knowledge of how texts and ICT databases are organised and acknowledging sources;

3 make notes in different ways, choosing a form which suits the purpose, e. g. *diagrammatic notes, making notes during a video, abbreviating for speed and ease of retrieval;*

4 review their developing skills as active, critical readers who search for meaning using a range of reading strategies;

5 trace the development of themes, values or ideas in texts;

6 recognise bias and objectivity, distinguishing facts from hypotheses, theories or opinions;

7 identify the ways implied and explicit meanings are conveyed in different texts, e.g. *irony, satire;*

8 investigate how meanings are changed when information is presented in different forms or transposed into different media;

11 investigate the different ways familiar themes are explored and presented by different writers;

Writing level

1 experiment with different approaches to planning, drafting, proofreading and presenting writing, taking account of the time available;

3 use writing for thinking and learning by recording ideas as they develop to aid reflection and problem solving;

6 experiment with figurative language in conveying a sense of character and setting;

7 experiment with different language choices to imply meaning and to establish the tone of a piece, e.g. *ironic, indignant;*

8 develop an imaginative or unusual treatment of familiar material or established conventions, e.g. u*pdating traditional tales;*

10 organise and present information, selecting and synthesising appropriate material and guiding the reader clearly through the text, e.g. *a technological process, an information leaflet;*

11 explain complex ideas and information clearly, e.g. *defining principles, explaining a scientific process;*

12 describe an event, process or situation, using language with an appropriate degree of formality, e.g. *a school prospectus;*

13 present a case persuasively, making selective use of evidence, using appropriate rhetorical devices and anticipating responses and objections;

14 develop and signpost arguments in ways that make the logic clear to the reader;

16 weigh different viewpoints and present a balanced analysis of an event or issue, e.g. *an environmental issue or historical investigation;*

17 integrate evidence into writing to support analysis or conclusions, e.g. *data, quotation;*

Speaking and Listening

5 ask questions to clarify understanding and refine ideas;

10 use talk to question, hypothesise, speculate, evaluate, solve problems and develop thinking about complex issues and ideas;

11 recognise and build on other people's contributions;

15 explore and develop ideas, issues and relationships through work in role.

This section of *Presenting the Past Book Two* (pages 4–38) relates to the QCA Scheme of Work unit 'Elizabeth I: how successfully did she tackle the problems of her reign?'

Presenting the Past Book Two unit title	Opportunities for Citizenship (National Curriculum for KS3)	Opportunities for Literacy (QCA *Framework*)	Key Skills	Opportunities for ICT	Thinking Skills
Who were the Tudors?	1a, b, d	7r9, **8**r6, 7, w5			
What was Europe like on 17 November 1558?	1g, i	7r6, 8, **8**r4	C, PS		
What did Europe seem like to Elizabeth I on 17 November 1558?	1a, c, i	7r6, 6, **8**r4	C		
What should Elizabeth do first?	1a, d, i	7s12, r2, 4, w3, 14, **8**r3, w10	C, PS, WO	✓	✓
Hunting for a husband?	1d, i	7r2, 4, 6,8, 9, w11, **8**r1, 4–6, w10	C, PS, WO		
Why was religion a matter of life and death?	1b, g, i	7s12, r1, w11, 12, **8**s4, r2, w10, 11	PS		
How did Catholics and Protestants disagree?	1b	7r4, 6, 8, **8**r3–5	PS		
Religion – how did Elizabeth compromise?	1a, b, g	7s8, r1, 2, 6, w12, **8**s7, r1, 5, w8, 10	C, PS		
Marriage at last?	1a, h	7r2, 6, 8-10, **8**r4, 6	C, WO		✓
Why was Mary Queen of Scots such a problem for Elizabeth?	1a, d, g	7s8, r2, 6, 7, 9, w11, 14, 15, 16, **8**s1, 5, r4, w10, 13, 14	C, PS,		✓
Why was Philip II of Spain such a problem for Elizabeth?	1g, i	7s12, r2, 4, 6, w2, 11, 15, **8**s1, r1, 4, w3, 13	C, PS	✓	✓
The Spanish Armada: How good was Philip's plan?	1g, i	7s8, 12, r1, w1, 14, **8**s6, 7, 12, 13, r1, w6, 7, 8, 12	C, PS, WO		✓
A Spanish view of the Armada	1g, i	7r2, 3, 6, w14, **8**s2, 12, r1, 4, 6, 8, 11, w8, 12, 16	PS	✓	✓
Catholics or Puritans?	1a, b, g, i	7s12, r1, 6, w2, 3, 18, sl10, 13, 14, **8**s7, r1, w13, 16, 17, sl10, 11	C, PS, WO		✓
How did Elizabeth deal with poor people and beggars?	1a, b, c	7r2, 6, 9, w3, 15, **8**r4, w3, 8, 13	C, PS, WO		✓
How successfully did Elizabeth tackle the problems of her reign?	1a, d, g, i	7r2, 4, w3, sl1, 10, 12, 13, r1, 2, 4 w3, **8**r3, 13, 16, w3, 16, sl5, 6, 10,	C, PS, WO	✓	✓

Key:

Explanations for National Curriculum Citizenship and QCA *Framework for teaching English: Years 7, 8, and 9* abbreviations can be found on page 5 and 6 of this book.

Key Skills abbreviations: C = Communication; PS = Problem Solving; WO = Working with Others

This unit provides a good opportunity to build on the prior learning of book one with an understanding of late medieval monarchy and how it evolved into the type of constitutional monarchy we have today through the study of a series of historical situations. This will include aspects such as religion, power, royal justice, punishment and legal systems, warfare and rights. From the beginning of Elizabeth's reign to the Stuarts, pupils will identify the characteristics of the Tudor monarchy and what Elizabeth did in order to survive and be remembered as a successful monarch.

Who were the Tudors? (Worksheet 1.1)

◆ This section begins with an overview of the Tudor dynasty as seen through the eyes of an old woman – Old Meg – and leads into a broader overview of Europe in 1558.

◆ This short input is supported by a family picture gallery of the Tudors to enable pupils to visualise the link between each of the Tudors and their interrelationship. You may wish to supplement the family tree with a precis for each person, highlighting two key points about each person such as how successful they were in a particular aspect of their reign.

◆ Worksheet 1.1 provides a blank family tree to aid pupils in their understanding of the Tudors.

What was Europe like on 17 November 1558?

◆ Here we see a broad overview of Europe in 1558. The map can be enlarged to enable pupils to access the 'bigger picture' from a European perspective at the start of Elizabeth's reign.

◆ The activity within this section is a compare and contrast exercise of the political situation in Europe in 1558, with Europe in other periods. Pupils might undertake a comparative study of European states as they existed in 1558 and as they are now, for example, where was the balance of power in 1558? Where is the balance of power in Europe today?

◆ Citizenship: you might discuss the concept of balance of power, what it is, what it includes, why it was necessary to have a balance of power.

◆ There is also scope for atlas work here.

17 November 1558: what problems did Elizabeth see?

◆ This activity is a warm-up task leading into the study of Elizabeth's problems.

◆ Citizenship: you might wish to revisit, through a context discussion, the rights and responsibilities of a monarch, or within a school, as an introduction to the activity.

◆ Within this section there is the opportunity for a differentiated activity with varying degrees of support. For example, you might look at what a particular monarch, such as Henry VIII, faced in terms of problems and how he resolved them.

What should Elizabeth do first? (W 1.2, 1.3)

◆ You might take group feedback on the problems Elizabeth faced, identifying or prioritising the most important problems. Which should she deal with first and why?

◆ Literacy: students develop an understanding of key words related to Elizabeth. Spellings and understanding of these words can be developed as homework activities or as part of an end-of-unit assessment.

◆ Extension activity: more-able pupils could choose three words and include them in sentences that describe Elizabeth and her problems in 1558. Are there any other possible problems not identified so far which might appear later?

◆ Worksheet 1.2 is provided to enable pupils to prioritise and group Elizabeth's problems. Worksheet 1.3 allows lower-ability pupils to access this task.

Hunting for a Husband (W 1.4, 1.5)

◆ In this section pupils learn about the importance of holding onto power for Elizabeth, her need to achieve security through alliances, the need for an heir to continue the Tudor line, the contemporary belief that a queen needed a husband to help her rule and, therefore, the pressure Elizabeth was under to marry. Pupils might compare modern royal marriages with the type of marriage expected for Elizabeth.

◆ Worksheet 1.4 is based on the task on page 15 of the student book.

◆ The tasks may be approached in several ways but lend themselves to a card sort exercise (see worksheet 1.5).

◆ An interview exercise could be undertaken with pupils taking on the identity of each candidate. Some appropriate questions might be set by the class and presented to each candidate in turn. This activity would support key skills.

◆ Paired work or group work might culminate in a role-play of the interview using a chat show or 'blind date' format. Final decisions choosing the most appropriate candidate could be presented in written form, through a panel spokesperson, or as a task in exercise books, perhaps leading to a class presentation highlighting the advantages/disadvantages of each candidate.

Why was religion a matter of life and death ?

◆ Pupils need to identify why religion was so important to people in the Tudor period

◆ A warm-up activity might relate to why religion is still a cause of dispute and conflict today e.g., in Ireland, the Middle East and the Balkans. You might address the issue of Britain as a multi-faith society and why the monarch is head of the Church of England.

◆ You might look back at the section in *Presenting the Past Book One: 1500–1750* on the Church in Medieval Britain, comparing and contrasting with the Church's role in the Tudor period.

How did Catholics and Protestants disagree? (W 1.6)

◆ This activity identifies similarities and differences between Catholics and Protestants in terms of their practices and beliefs. There is the opportunity to bring in a comparison of other faiths where appropriate.

- A DARTS-style activity is provided to aid lower-ability pupils.
- Class discussion on this unit could include the 'what if..?' factor, i.e., 'what if Elizabeth had been a Catholic/married Philip of Spain?' Pupils might discuss the religion of Elizabeth and how and why it affected the government of the country, to establish that history is often affected by the personal views of the monarch.

Religion – how did Elizabeth compromise? (W1.7)

- The activity identifies how religion changed according to the beliefs held by each Tudor monarch.
- Worksheet 1.7 provides a writing frame activity which will help with this text analysis.

Marriage at last (W1.8)

- Here the theme is whether Elizabeth should be forced into marriage and what the criteria of a 'good' husband were.
- Pupils may revisit the earlier marriage role-play exercise, introducing here Francois, Duke of Alençon.
- You might highlight how the criteria of a 'good husband' changed according to who was doing the choosing. This is delivered through task 1 on p.21.
- Pupils should be aware that Elizabeth was furious because she demanded respect and would not accept criticism of her personal choices (especially from a social inferior), as such criticism would make her look weak. (Worksheet 1.8).

Mary Queen of Scots: why was she such a problem for Elizabeth? (W 1.9)

- It may be advisable to refer back to the family tree at the beginning of the section and highlight why Elizabeth regarded Mary as such a threat to her crown.
- Pupils are encouraged to put themselves in Elizabeth's shoes and decide what they think she should do about Mary.
- Worksheet 1.9 provides a DARTS-style activity to help with this text analysis.

Philip II of Spain: why was he such a problem for Elizabeth? (W 1.10, 1.11)

- The focus here is the personal rivalry between Elizabeth and Philip. It is very important for pupils to understand why Philip was regarded as such a threat by Elizabeth. This is supported by worksheet 1.10.
- Worksheet 1.11 provides pupils with the opportunity to write up a C.V. for Elizabeth and Philip. Pupils can decide who had the most impressive track record.
- Extension activity: look at each monarch in a broader perspective, for example, what did they do for the poor? How did they stimulate trade? Who were their chief allies?
- Less-able pupils might undertake the role of historians and research Elizabeth and Philip using CD-ROMs or the internet.

The Spanish Armada: how good was Philip's plan? (W 1.12)

- Pupils are asked to investigate what really happened to the Armada (worksheet 1.12).
- Students can also write a letter explaining why the Armada failed.

- Working in pairs pupils could give both an English and then a Spanish perspective on this.

A Spanish view of the Armada (w 1.13, 1.14)

- The cartoon giving the Spanish version of events on pp 31–33 of the student book gives pupils a good opportunity to compare the two different accounts of the same event.
- Pupils might write their own English or Spanish version of the Armada for a newspaper report using worksheet 1.13.
- Extension activity: the more-able might highlight reasons for the differences in the two accounts and look at other recent political or historical events which have different viewpoints.
- Worksheet 1.14 provides a timeline to support less-able pupils.

Catholics or Puritans?

- This section looks at who was the bigger threat to Elizabeth's church. Pupils undertake a comparative exercise, using a living graph, looking at how Catholics and Puritans were treated at different points during Elizabeth's reign. Using worksheet 1.15, pupils could construct their own version of the graph and compare each other's work.
- A class discussion might consider the different reasons why Elizabeth's treatment of Catholics and Puritans varied during her reign, how each religious group constituted a political threat to Elizabeth and how Elizabeth dealt with other problems during her reign, such as social and economic issues. This will lead into the final sections.

How did Elizabeth deal with poor people and beggars?

- Here pupils see that Elizabeth was not as compassionate in dealing with the poor as society today.
- Pupils may carry out a role-play exercise interviewing someone applying for relief with pupils asking their own questions.
- Worksheet 1.16 asks pupils to produce a written report outlining recommendations on the treatment of beggars.
- Extension activity: pupils might look back at their work on the poor in the Medieval period and compare this treatment with Elizabeth's.

How successfully did Elizabeth tackle the problems of her reign?

- Here, pupils review the work undertaken during this section.
- The activities pupils complete require a DARTs activity. Pupils will need to think about how successful she was 'on balance'. You might lead a class discussion into what the terms 'successful' and 'unsuccessful' mean, i.e., did helping some poor people make Elizabeth successful, or should she have helped more poor people?
- Extension activity: a more detailed assessment of Elizabeth's reign. Pupils might consider Elizabeth's reign over the longer term, looking at issues she inherited (religious conflict) and the problems she left behind her (succession and relations with Scotland, France and Spain).

The Tudors

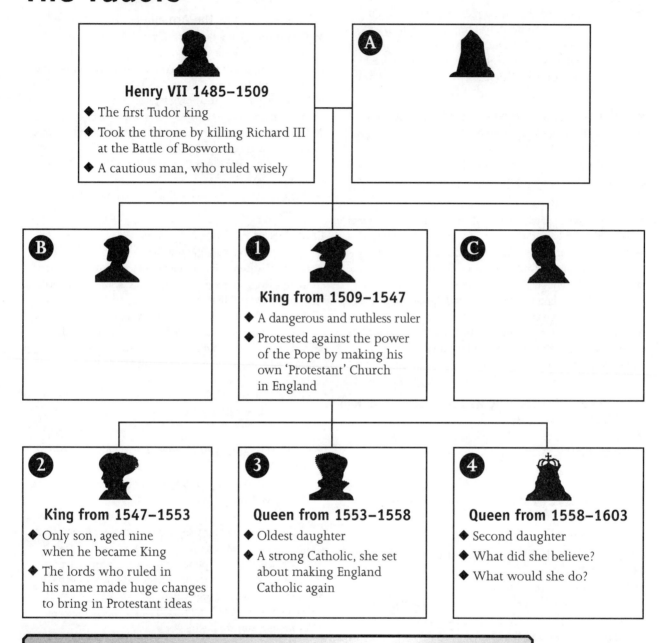

Henry VII 1485–1509
◆ The first Tudor king
◆ Took the throne by killing Richard III at the Battle of Bosworth
◆ A cautious man, who ruled wisely

A

B

1 **King from 1509–1547**
◆ A dangerous and ruthless ruler
◆ Protested against the power of the Pope by making his own 'Protestant' Church in England

C

2 **King from 1547–1553**
◆ Only son, aged nine when he became King
◆ The lords who ruled in his name made huge changes to bring in Protestant ideas

3 **Queen from 1553–1558**
◆ Oldest daughter
◆ A strong Catholic, she set about making England Catholic again

4 **Queen from 1558–1603**
◆ Second daughter
◆ What did she believe?
◆ What would she do?

Step 1

1 From the information provided under each box can you identify who is in boxes 1–4?

2 After the person in box 1, who is next in line to the throne?

3 How are the people in boxes 2 and 3 related?

4 Who are the missing figures in boxes **A**, **B**, & **C**?

Extension Activity

◆ How did the Tudors come to rule England?

◆ What problem is Elizabeth going to have at the end of her reign if she is childless?

What should Elizabeth do first? (1)

Step 1

1 In pairs, use this chart to help you decide which of Elizabeth's problems go together.

◆ In the second column write down which of the **Other Problems** you think go with each of the problems in the first column.

◆ Use the third column to explain why you think these two go together.

◆ You may find that the questions can be arranged in different ways.

A problem… →	And what about…? →	These go together because…
Should I hurry to appoint a new Archbishop of Canterbury?		
Should I marry and try to provide an heir?		
What should I do about the war with France?		
What should I do about poor people and beggars?		

Other Problems

◆ Should I continue burning Protestants? How should I treat them?

◆ How should I treat my ally King Philip?

◆ What should I do about money?

◆ What should I do about Scotland?

◆ What should I do about Ireland?

◆ Should I obey the Pope and keep the Church Catholic?

What should Elizabeth do first? (2)

Step 1

1 Work in pairs to decide how important Elizabeth's problems are.

◆ Cut-out Elizabeth's problems and place them on the fish, deciding how important each one is.

◆ **Remember:** The more urgent the problem, the nearer to the head of the fish it needs to be – the less urgent it is the nearer to the tail it can go.

◆ Should I hurry to appoint a new Archbishop of Canterbury?	◆ What should I do about money?
◆ Should I marry and try to provide an heir?	◆ What should I do about the war with France?
◆ What should I do about Scotland?	◆ What should I do about poor people and beggars?
◆ Should I continue burning Protestants?	◆ How should I treat my ally King Philip?
◆ What should I do about Ireland?	◆ Should I obey the Pope and keep the Church Catholic?

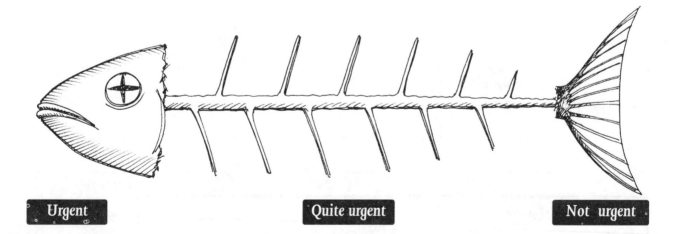

Urgent   Quite urgent   Not urgent

Step 2

2 When you have placed all your cards, compare your decisions with those of another group. Are there any you have put in the same place? Are there any you have put in a different order? Discuss the reasons for your choice.

Presenting the Past 2 Teacher's Resources © HarperCollins *Publishers* 2002

Hunting for a husband? (1)

Step 1

1 Look at the things that Elizabeth and Burghley think are important in a good husband, and read what each suitor says about himself. Using the chart, list the names of the four possible husbands in the order that both Elizabeth and Burghley would have preferred them.

2 Include the words listed below in the explanation you give for each choice and say whether they are positive or negative factors.

Elizabeth's Choice

1 Name: _____

because _____

2 Name: _____

because _____

3 Name: _____

because _____

4 Name: _____

because _____

Burghley's Choice

1 Name: _____

because _____

2 Name: _____

because _____

3 Name: _____

because _____

4 Name: _____

because _____

◆ Religion ◆ Looks ◆ Country ◆ Personality ◆ Wealth

My Choice

1 Name: _____

because _____

2 Name: _____

because _____

3 Name: _____

because _____

4 Name: _____

because _____

Step 2

3 Now put the four possible husbands in the order you think would have been best for Elizabeth. Again, use the words in the box in your answers and say whether they are positive or negative factors.

Hunting for a husband? (2)

Step 1

1 Using two colours underline the positive points (advantages) for each candidate in one colour and the negative points (disadvantages) in a different colour.

2 For each candidate use your coloured underlining to decide whether each suitor has more positive than negative points.

3 If you were Elizabeth, who would you choose?

K ♠

"I am Philip II, King of Spain. I am a strong, rich, Catholic ruler. I have no links with your English lords. I will protect you and England against France."

K ♦

"I am Charles, Archduke of Austria. I am a cousin of King Philip of Spain. I will help England stay friendly with Spain. I have no links with your English lords. I am a Catholic. People call me 'beautiful and well-faced'."

K ♣

"I am Prince Eric of Sweden. I am a Protestant. I have no links with your English lords. I have no lands of my own, so I won't drag England into other people's wars. People tell me I'm ugly."

K ♥

"I am Lord Robert Dudley. I am English. I am Protestant. I am strong, brave and good-looking. I know other lords are jealous of me and my family, but … I know you love me."

Presenting the Past 2 Teacher's Resources © HarperCollins *Publishers* 2002

How did Catholics and Protestants disagree?

If you were a Catholic, you believed that ...	If you were a Protestant, you believed that ...
◆ you must do what the Church teaches.	◆ you must obey the Bible.
◆ souls can go to purgatory – a place of punishment between heaven and hell.	◆ purgatory is not in the Bible, therefore it does not exist.
◆ the prayers of the living can help the souls of the dead to move out of purgatory and into heaven.	◆ praying for dead people is wrong and a waste of time, because it's too late to help them.
◆ the Church can help you to save your soul from hell.	◆ the Church cannot save your soul from hell. Only God can do this.
◆ you must **confess** [admit] your **sins** [wrong thoughts and actions] to a priest, and you must pray to the Virgin Mary and the saints for help.	◆ only God can help you get to heaven, not your priest.
◆ you must go to **Mass** [a special service], where bread and wine become the body and blood of Jesus. Only priests drink the wine because it is so special.	◆ in church, everyone takes bread and wine as a way of remembering Jesus. They do not physically change into His body and blood.
◆ the Pope is head of the Church everywhere, getting his power directly from God. He leads the bishops and priests, who help you to communicate with God.	◆ the Pope is not head of the Church, and the bishops and priests are not necessary for you to communicate with God.
◆ anyone who goes against the teaching of the Church can be burned as a heretic.	◆ you should follow important Protestant leaders like Martin Luther and John Calvin.

Step 1

1 In the boxes above highlight the similarities between Catholic and Protestant beliefs in one colour and the differences in another colour.

◆ What do you notice about how similar the ideas and beliefs of the Catholics and Protestants were?

◆ What do you notice about how different the ideas and beliefs of the Catholics and Protestants were?

Step 2

2 Now look at the pictures of the Catholic and Protestant churches. Draw a chart with two columns, label one **Protestants** and one **Catholics**. Fill in the columns with the labels from the churches. Colour features which are the same in each church in one colour, and features which are different in each church in a different colour.

◆ How different were the Catholic and Protestant churches?

◆ How similar were the Catholic and Protestant churches?

◆ Now look at the church from Elizabeth's reign on page 21. What do you notice about this church?

How did Elizabeth compromise?

Step 1

1 Imagine you are a Catholic living at the time of Elizabeth I. Using the ideas below and the information on pages 20–21 write a letter to a friend who lives abroad.

◆ Describe some of the **changes** that Elizabeth introduced into the Church.

◆ Describe some of the things in the Church that Elizabeth **did not change**.

◆ At the end of the letter describe your views and feelings about what Elizabeth has done.

◆ You could also write your letter from a Protestant viewpoint.

Dear _____

How are you? I hope you are well. There have been many changes here under the new Queen, especially in the church.

As a Catholic I do approve of some things about Elizabeth's church, such as
_____
_____
_____
_____

However, there are other things I do not fully approve of _____
_____
_____
_____
_____

There are also a few things which I have mixed feeling about _____
_____
_____
_____
_____

Overall, I think the new churches are _____
_____
_____
_____

Presenting the Past 2 Teacher's Resources © HarperCollins *Publishers* 2002

Hands off! Don't tell the Queen what to do!

Possible reasons for punishing Stubbs

Stubbs was a Puritan (an extreme Protestant).

Stubbs wrote about the Queen's marriage, which was forbidden by law.

Stubbs openly insulted the Queen.

Stubbs insulted Alençon.

Background information

Elizabeth disliked Puritans a lot and sometimes treated them harshly. Punishing one Puritan was an easy way of warning others not to cause trouble.

Elizabeth was a woman ruler who took great care to appear strong and in control. Her image could easily be damaged. She still believed she could have children.

Elizabeth stopped everyone debating possible marriages or who should succeed her. Some of her advisers may have encouraged Stubbs to publish his pamphlet in order to stop a foreign marriage they hated. Her answer was to punish Stubbs.

Elizabeth was probably in love with Alençon. She did not like being shown up in front of a foreign prince. An insult to Alençon was also an insult to his brother, the King of France.

Possible factors affecting Elizabeth's decision

 the Queen's personal feelings

 a threat to her power

 both of these

Step 1

1 Draw a table with three columns and four rows. In a group place the four 'Reason' cards in column one. In column two match up the 'background information' with the 'reason' cards.

2 Now, putting the factor cards in column three, decide if the reasons and background information you have in columns one and two: upset the Queen's personal feelings; are a threat to her power; or are both of the above.

3 Compare your answers with another group. Are they the same? Are they Different?

4 Why do you think Queen Elizabeth was angry with Stubbs?

What shall I do with Mary?

Step 1

1 Use the chart below and what you have learnt to help Elizabeth decide what to do with Mary Queen of Scots.

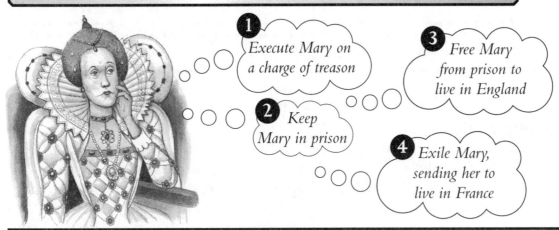

1 Execute Mary on a charge of treason

2 Keep Mary in prison

3 Free Mary from prison to live in England

4 Exile Mary, sending her to live in France

1 I could execute Mary, which would help me because _____
Although a problem with doing this might be _____

2 I could keep Mary alive, which would help me because _____
However, a problem with doing this might be _____

3 I could free Mary, which would help me because _____
A problem with doing this might be _____

4 I could send Mary into exile, which would help me because _____
On the other hand a problem with doing this might be _____

5 Do <u>you</u> think Elizabeth did the right thing? Use the sentences below to help you with your answer.

I think the best option was _____, because _____

I think the worst option was _____, because _____

I think Elizabeth's decision to execute Mary was _____,
because _____

Extension Activity

2 Imagine you are Mary. Write a letter to Elizabeth pleading for her help. Include in your letter:

◆ Your view of each of Elizabeth's four options. Which option would you recommend to Elizabeth?

◆ The ways in which you could help Elizabeth so that she would see you as a friend and not as a threat.

Was Elizabeth guilty of Murder?

On 1st February 1587 she sent her secretary, Davison, to bring the warrant. He hid it in the middle of a pile of other papers, hoping that would make it easier for her to sign it.

While she signed the papers, she chatted about the weather. She then told Davison to take the warrant to Walsingham.

Elizabeth gave instructions that the execution should take place indoors, out of sight of the public. She was not to be told anything about it until afterwards.

She sent a private letter to Mary's gaoler, asking him to quietly murder Mary.

On the 8th February, Mary was executed. Elizabeth was furious. She accused her advisers of acting without her direct permission.

She denied responsibility for Mary's death.

She refused to see Lord Burghley for weeks, imprisoned Davison in the Tower of London and fined him £10,000, wrecking his career.

She wore black clothes in Mary's memory and ordered a royal funeral in Peterborough Cathedral.

Step 1

1 Using a coloured pen, underline any words which tell you that Elizabeth was worried, nervous, concerned or feeling guilty about the execution of Mary Queen of Scots.
Remember: Mary was Elizabeth's cousin and a fellow queen.

2 List five of the words you have chosen in the spaces below:

1 _____	4 _____
2 _____	5 _____
3 _____	

Step 2

3 Now write five sentences and include a different one of your chosen words in each sentence to describe how Elizabeth might have <u>really</u> felt about the execution of her cousin Mary.

1 _____

2 _____

3 _____

4 _____

5 _____

Curriculum Vitae

Step 1

1 Using what you have learnt about Mary and Philip fill out three copies of the C.V. below, one each for Mary, Philip, and Elizabeth. Working in a group of three, decide who you think posed the greater threat to Elizabeth. Was it Philip or Mary?

Curriculum Vitae:

Last name .... D.O.B ....
First name .... Address ....
....
....
....

Country of origin ....
Current occupation ....
Religion .... Marital status ....

My greatest achievement so far is ....
....
....

Personal ambitions: I would like to become ....
....
....
....

My greatest fear is ....
....
....
....

Step 2

2 Use this writing frame to help you answer the question 'Who was the greater threat to Elizabeth?'
I think _____ was the greater threat to Elizabeth because
_____
_____
_____

Plot the route of the Armada

Step 1

1 Use the blank map, and information on pages 28–30 to plot the route of the Armada. *As you plot the route, show some of the problems the Armada faced on the way (e.g. poor weather and attacks by the English).*

On your map use symbols to show:

◆ a storm
◆ a wreck
◆ an attack
◆ a fire

Include a key to explain your symbols.

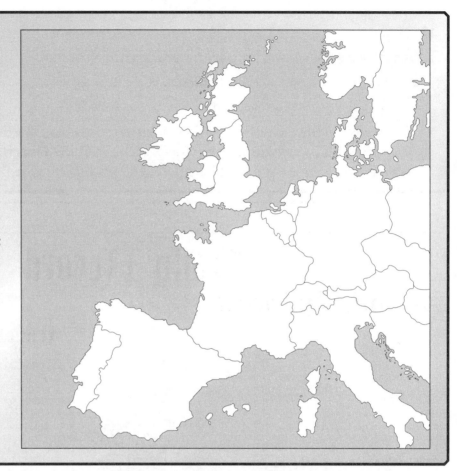

Step 2

2 List three key reasons why the Armada failed to land in England:

a _____

b _____

c _____

3 Now, imagine you are an officer on one of the Spanish ships. Write a letter to Philip explaining why the Armada didn't achieve its aim. Include the key reasons you identified which caused the Armada to fail. You might add what you think could have helped the Spanish to be successful in their invasion attempt.

Your Royal Highness,

_____

_____

_____

_____

Armada Defeated!

Step 1

1 Using what you have learnt, put together a newspaper report of either

   a An English newspaper account of the defeat of the Armada; or

   b A Spanish newspaper account of the failure of the Armada.

◆ The headlines for each of the two sections in the account are done for you.
You may wish to include an eye-witness account of the invasion in your report.
Remember: your account will be different depending on which view you choose.

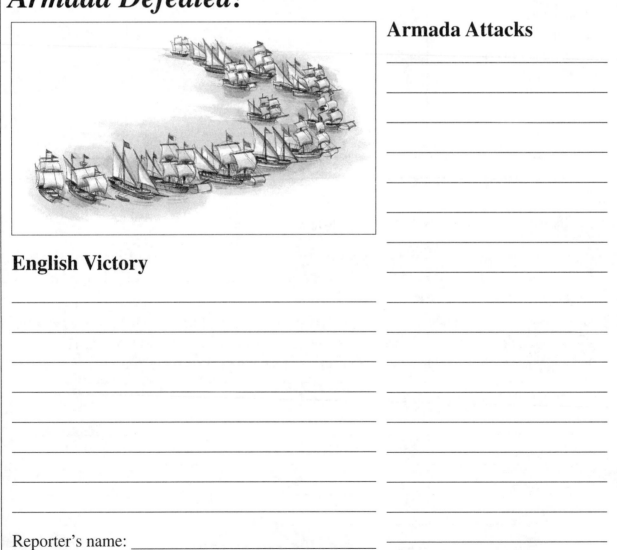

15th September, 1588

Daily Record

Armada Defeated!

Armada Attacks

_____

_____

_____

_____

_____

_____

_____

English Victory

_____

_____

_____

_____

_____

_____

_____

Reporter's name: _____

How the Armada was defeated

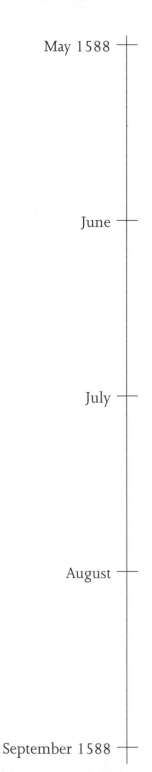

May 1588

June

July

August

September 1588

Step 1

1 Using the information from your map and your newspaper account, complete the timeline showing the key events in the Armada's attempt to invade England.

Who suffered most during Elizabeth's reign?

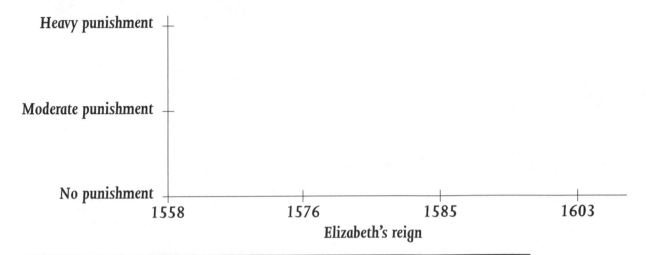

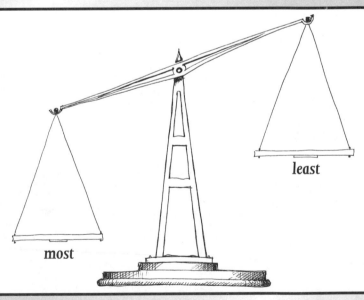

least

most

Poor people and beggars

Request for Financial Support

REQUEST FOR FINANCIAL SUPPORT

Name _____

Occupation _____

Born locally   yes / no / don't know

Financial condition _____

When did he last work? _____

Why does he not have work now? _____

Overseer's recommendation:
                   deserving poor / undeserving poor

because _____

I recommend that he _____

Signed _____
OVERSEER OF THE POOR

How successfully did Elizabeth tackle the problems of her reign?

Step 1

1 Look at the lists of points in the boxes on pages 38–39. Decide which points in each list prove Elizabeth was **successful**, and which points prove she was **unsuccessful**. Use the tables below to help you list the points. You might like to use a different colour for each column.

Marriage

successful	unsuccessful

Religion

successful	unsuccessful

Mary Queen of Scots

successful	unsuccessful

Philip of Spain

successful	unsuccessful

Poor people and beggars

successful	unsuccessful

Other problems

successful	unsuccessful

Step 2

2 Overall, how successfully do you think Elizabeth dealt with the problems of her reign? Use your completed charts to help you answer this question.

This section of *Presenting the Past Book Two* (pages 39–67) relates to the QCA Scheme of Work unit 'The civil wars: was England 'turned upside down' in the seventeenth century?'

Presenting the Past Book Two unit title	Opportunities for Citizenship (National Curriculum for KS3)	Opportunities for Literacy (QCA *Framework*)	Key Skills	Opportunities for ICT	Thinking Skills
Who were the Stuarts?	1b, i	7r1, 8r4			
Charles I: the world turned upside down?	1h	7r1, 8r4	C, PS, WO	✔	✔
What did successful rulers do?	1a, d, i	7w2, **8**r3, w3	C, PS		
Meet the King	1a, b, d, g	7r2, 6, 8, w2, 15, 16, **8**r3, 4, w13	C, PS		
Who fought whom in the Civil War?	1b, d, g	7r2, 6, **8**r5	C, PS, WO		✔
"This war without an enemy"?	1b, c, d, f, g	7r2, 4, 6, 7, **8**r3, 5	PS, WO	✔	
Were the King's enemies bound to fall out?	1a-d, f, g	7r2, 6, 8, w3, 11, 15, **8**r4, 5, w14	C, PS, WO	✔	✔
How united was the New Model Army?	1a-d, f, g	7r2, 6, 8, 9, **8**r4	C, PS, WO		✔
1649: who held power now?	1a-g	7r1, 2, 6, **8**r2, 5	C, PS, WO	✔	✔
Why do historians and film makers tell the same story differently?	1a-g	7r2, 6, 8, 10, w2, 5, 15, sl10, 12, 13,**8**r1, 3, 4, 11, w8, 14, 16, sl5, 10, 11	C, PS, WO	✔	✔
Was Oliver Cromwell a 'war criminal'?	1a-g	7r2, 4, 6, 8-10, w2, 12, 15, 16, 18, **8**r3-8, 11, w3, 10, 13, 14, 16, 17	C, PS, WO		✔
What happened after Cromwell died?	1a, b, g, h,	7r2, 6, 9, w16, 18, **8**r1, 5, 6, w14, 16	C, PS		✔

Key:

Explanations for National Curriculum Citizenship and QCA *Framework for teaching English: Years 7, 8, and 9* abbreviations can be found on page 5 and 6 of this book.

Key Skills abbreviations: C = Communication; PS = Problem Solving; WO = Working with Others

This section addresses the fate of the Stuart Monarchy and the outcome of the English Civil War by looking at the power of the monarchy, the role of Parliament, the importance of religion and the character and personality of Charles I and Oliver Cromwell. Pupils will develop an understanding of how and why the English Civil War happened and what the consequences were for the Stuart Monarchy and the power of Parliament. Aspects of Citizenship are very much reinforced throughout this unit. Rights and responsibilities and political literacy are a particular focus. This includes the role of the established Church as an instrument of social control, the importance of the concept of Divine Right of Kings, the political significance of Church leaders and the role of religion in fomenting social and political unrest.

Who were the Stuarts?

◆ This page will enable you to activate prior learning through linking the end of Elizabeth's reign with the accession of the Stuarts. Similarities and differences between Elizabeth and Charles I are highlighted by assessing how successful they were as monarchs.

◆ The family tree provides pupils with a visible link between the Tudors and the Stuarts.

Charles I: The world turned upside down?

◆ The significance of the English Civil War continues to be a debating point amongst historians, was it a civil war or a revolution? Pupils have the opportunity to investigate both the long- and short-term significance of the English Civil War in this section.

What did successful rulers do? (Worksheet 2.1)

◆ You might revisit the section in book one on what makes a 'successful' monarch as a warm-up activity. Working in groups, pupils could make a list of what makes a 'good' Headteacher, Football Manager or Prime Minister and then relate it to a good monarch in the 17th century. Some ideas are presented on page 43 but you may wish to hold these back until the groups feed their ideas into the whole class discussion.

◆ Worksheet 2.1 allows pupils to access the concept of what makes a successful ruler and draw on prior knowledge.

Meet the King (w 2.2, 2.3)

◆ There is the opportunity to undertake a structured role-play covering an interview with Charles I, with a member of the class or the class teacher taking on the role of the King. The class might also consider what some of Charles's responses would be using worksheet 2.2.

◆ The audience might have a vote to rate Charles's performance using a score card or a clap-o-meter, indicating audience satisfaction with Charles's performance. A large cardboard version of the success-o-meter, as presented on page 45, could be produced by the teacher.

◆ More-able pupils could script their own interview or produce their own set of questions. Again, this could take the form of a political news interview or a chat show format. Using worksheet 2.3 pupils can also look at how successful Charles was compared with two other 17th century kings.

◆ You might bring in the BBC *History File* Series on the Stuarts and/or an extract of the film *Cromwell* showing a small clip of Charles I.

The Civil War: Who's Who? (w 2.4, 2.5)

◆ It is important to supplement this section with key words and phrases which support conceptual understanding, especially in respect of the views and ideas of 17th century monarchy (i.e., the Divine Right of Kings, Great Chain of Being and religious conformity). This could be done through a series of word walls, 'splat mats' and other strategies that link in with the NLS. Worksheet 2.4 can be used for this purpose.

◆ Pupils should understand exactly who was on which side – who supported the king and who supported Parliament. Using the card sort exercise on worksheet 2.5, pupils can work out whose side a particular group would be on. The class-teacher will need to highlight some of the ambiguities and contradictions here – for example not all of the gentry supported the King.

'This War without an enemy'? (w 2.6)

◆ Mapping skills are used here to identify areas which supported the King and areas which supported Parliament.

◆ Extension activity: pupils might undertake a more detailed analysis of geographical support considering the influences of Social, Economic and Religious factors and identifying any trends or common characteristics.

◆ Using worksheet 2.6 pupils can produce a timeline of events leading up to the outbreak of the Civil War and/or the events between 1642 and 1646, using pages 49–50 to support the activities. This will enable pupils to understand the long- and short-term causes of the Civil War and how the actions and intentions of Charles and Parliament contributed to the outbreak of war.

Were the King's enemies bound to fall out? (w 2.7)

◆ Again, there is the opportunity to undertake some map work (worksheet 2.7) and produce some diagrammatic representations of events between 1642 and 1648. Pupils might place battles/key events/key people onto a map to show the course of the war and the key events. VAK accelerated learning strategies are a key learning tool here.

How united was the New Model Army? (w 2.8)

◆ The focus here is on how opinions differed about what to do with Charles at the end of the Civil War.

◆ Pupils have the opportunity to investigate the different options open to Cromwell at the end of the war. The class teacher may wish to divide the class into smaller groups and give them one particular option (i.e., execute the king). The group can then produce a list of advantages and disadvantages for their particular option.

◆ This task ties in with extended writing structures, an example of which is provided on worksheet 2.8.

◆ Pupils might also consider the causes and consequences of each argument put forward by the officer and soldier. You could highlight the hypothesis – 'With the execution of Charles I all power was held by Cromwell'. Evidence to prove or disprove this hypothesis can be given out in the form of pictures or written source material.

Who held power now? (w 2.9)

◆ Pupils might perform a role-play or dramatic reconstruction of the execution of Charles I. The action could be frozen just before the axe falls. Using worksheet 2.9 pupils can think about what the various people present at the scene are thinking (i.e., Charles, Cromwell, Bishop Juxon, the executioner, the soldier on the front row, the little boy).

Why do historians and film makers tell the same story differently? (w 2.10, 2.11)

◆ This section encourages pupils to question the nature of historical interpretation, through a comparative study of the execution of Charles I and the film *Cromwell*.

◆ Again, you may wish to use clips from the film *Cromwell*, but usage of these types of media needs to be short and focused.

◆ The picture storyboard presents a narrative of the execution of Charles I. Each picture could be presented separately allowing pupils to construct their own version of the execution of Charles I.

◆ This activity also provides a lead into a role-play on the execution of Charles using a 'freezeframe' approach where students are asked to consider the thoughts of each person on the execution platform or amongst the crowd at the precise moment of Charles's execution.

◆ Using worksheet 2.10 pupils can compare another version of the execution with the film and historian accounts. The DARTS activity here will make the comparison more accessible to lower-ability pupils.

◆ The pupil activity on page 59 enables pupils to compare and contrast the two versions of the event. More-able pupils might wish to identify other historical events and undertake a further study that focuses upon historical and film interpretations, for example *Braveheart*, *Rob Roy* or *The Patriot* (worksheet 2.11). Less-able pupils might complete fewer of the questions included on the grid.

◆ Through modelling of this exercise pupils will gain a high level understanding of the concept of interpretation. Pupils may ask further relevant questions which will raise issues of accuracy versus dramatic effect/fact versus fiction.

Was Oliver Cromwell a war criminal? (w 2.12)

◆ In this section pupils look at the actions and intentions of Oliver Cromwell during the Civil War and find him not guilty of war crimes (by today's standards or those of the 17th century). Worksheet 2.12 will help pupils to answer this question.

◆ Pupils could either be presented with an hypothesis or the more-able might formulate and test their own hypothesis on Cromwell.

◆ Another approach might be to undertake a role-play with Cromwell on trial for his actions and members of the class taking on the role of judge, jury, witnesses and counsel for the defence/prosecution. You may wish to include witnesses such as the rebels at Burford, the Levellers and the Diggers as well as Irish Catholics.

◆ Preparation for this section is essential to ensure that students can fully consider the issues. Careful reading of the text is also essential.

◆ The activity may be managed so that one or more groups produce a favourable 'not guilty' judgement on Cromwell, whilst other groups return the opposite verdict.

What happened after Cromwell died? (w 2.13, 2.14)

◆ Here, pupils look at events after Cromwell's death. The narrative considers the feelings and emotions of a puritan Cromwellian supporter.

◆ The activity is based upon an extended writing exercise which outlines how people felt on the death of Cromwell. Some headings and an extension have been provided on worksheet 2.13 to help pupils with their exercise. Worksheet 2.14 encourages pupils to think from an alternative point of view and create a living graph to illustrate this.

◆ The final part of this section prepares the student for the study of the overthrow of the Stuarts in the Glorious Revolution of 1688–89. Pupils are encouraged to think again about how people felt on the restoration of the Stuart monarchy in 1660, for which other historical accounts of the Restoration may be useful.

◆ Extension activity: (worksheet 2.15) more-able pupils might research answers to other summary hypotheses, i.e, what was the role of Parliament in governing the country? Why was the Church so important in all aspects of society?

The DOs and DON'Ts of being a successful ruler

Step 1

1 Using the success diagram on page 43, decide with a partner the five most important things a successful ruler must do. You can also look back at the end of the section on Elizabeth and her problems to help you.

Five easy steps to being a great monarch!

This is a quick and easy guide to being a successful ruler. Follow the tips below and you can't fail.

The five most important things a successful ruler **must** do:

◆ _____

◆ _____

◆ _____

◆ _____

◆ _____

But you must avoid making any of the big mistakes listed below.

Three things a successful ruler **must not** do:

◆ _____

◆ _____

◆ _____

Step 2

1 There are also things a successful ruler just would not do. Look again at the diagram on page 43 and decide which would be the three biggest mistakes any monarch could make if he/she wanted to hold on to their crown. List these above.

2 What advice would you give Charles I when he became king in 1625?

Presenting the Past 2 Teacher's Resources © HarperCollins *Publishers* 2002

An interview with Charles I

Step 1

1 Imagine you are the reporter interviewing King Charles I. Fill out the report below.

Name of interviewer _____

Title of TV/radio programme _____

_____

Interview Questions: **Answers:**

◆ How does it feel to be king?

◆ What are your two key aims as king?

◆ Who would you say are your enemies?

◆ Who would you say are your friends?

◆ What are your views on:
   1 Religion
   2 Ireland
   3 Puritans
   4 Tax
   5 Money

Two further questions I would like to ask are:

◆

◆

Step 2

2 Having asked your questions and listened to Charles' answers, decide the following using the writing frame to help you:

   a How would you rate Charles as a King?

   b Do you think Charles is going to stir up trouble for himself and the country?

I think Charles is going to be a (good/bad*) king.

I think Charles will rule the country (wisely/unwisely*) because

_____

Delete as appropriate.

Gustavus Adolphus of Sweden and Henry IV of France

Step 1

1 Read the two accounts from 17th century kings below.

Adolphus of Sweden

I became King of Sweden in 1611, when I was 17 years old. My country was weak and poor. I soon set out to change all that.

1 I reorganised the government and made it much more efficient.

2 I sold our copper to the Dutch and this helped make the country rich.

3 I was a brilliant soldier. Sweden always beat its enemies in Denmark, Poland and Germany. As Protestants, we defended German Protestants against German Catholics. My armies won new lands for Sweden, and people called me the 'Lion of the North'.

4 When I died in battle at the age of 38, Sweden was strong and respected, but ...

n although selling copper made my country richer, my government owed lots of money because my wars were so expensive.

n Taxes were high and some of my royal lands had to be sold off.

n Sweden's enemies were jealous of our gains. My country had to fight more wars after my death.

Henry IV of France

Before I became King, France was torn apart by civil war between Catholics and Protestants. Instead of fighting foreigners, the people were fighting each other! I led the Protestants. However, when I did become king in 1589, Catholics would not accept me, and Paris shut its gates against my army.

My best idea was to change my religion and become a Catholic. A lot of French Catholics then supported me. Next, I had to fight the Spanish, who still had soldiers in France to help the Catholics. I fought the Spanish so hard, they left the country.

With France now at peace, I tried to stay out of wars, and encourage trade. This got the government out of debt. I also gave Protestants some rights to worship freely and protect themselves.

I was really popular. It was a shame I was killed by a maniac in 1610.

Step 2

2 How does each of these two kings compare to the success wheel for a 17th century ruler on page 43? Which one do you think was the most successful?

3 Using the information on pages 44–47 and the two accounts above, which king do you think was the most successful – Adolphus, Henry IV or Charles I?

Key words on Charles I and the English Civil War

Divine Right of Kings	Tax
Toleration	Roundhead
Civil War	Monarchy
Parliament	Puritan
Papist	Government
Catholics	Cavalier

Church of England

Step 1

These are all key words, phrases and concepts that you will encounter during this unit of work. Some are about religion, some are about government and some are about conflict.

1 *As you work through this section look out for these words and phrases and make a note of what they mean to help you understand this section of work more clearly.*

2 *Divide your notes into three sections labelled;* **religion**, **government** *and* **conflict** *and place the words or phrases and their meanings under the correct heading.*

The Civil War: whose side are you on?

The King

God made me King.
I run the government.
I make peace and war.
Taxes are for me to spend.
I agree to new laws.
I control the soldiers and sailors.
I call Parliament when I want.
All the rich people support me.

Parliament

The House of Lords   **The House of Commons**

We are all the
bishops and the
Lords of England and
Wales. We help
make new laws.

We are the Members of
Parliament (MPs). We are
ordinary men, with no title,
though we are all fairly rich.
Other rich men choose us to
be MPs. We help make new
laws. Only we can agree to
new taxes for the King.

A Puritan	An Anglican	A merchant tradesman
A member of the aristocracy and landed gentry	A poor farmer in Yorkshire	A Scottish labourer

Step 1

1 Use the form below to create your own guide to the medieval Church. Start by
   looking back at the pictures of hell on page 57 of your textbook. In the same style as
   these pictures, draw your own picture of what your personal idea of hell would be.

Charles's days are numbered...

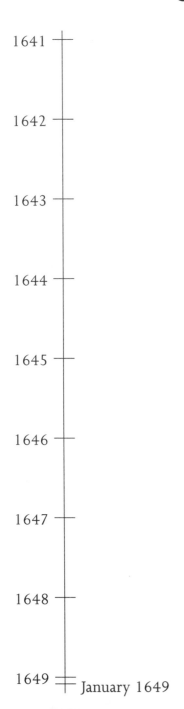

1641

1642

1643

1644

1645

1646

1647

1648

1649 — January 1649

Step 1

1 Mark on this timeline the key events of the English Civil War from when Charles I raised his Standard at Nottingham, until his execution at Whitehall in London in January 1649.

2 Use the information from pages 44–55 and any other information you find to construct your timeline.

Were the King's enemies bound to fall out?

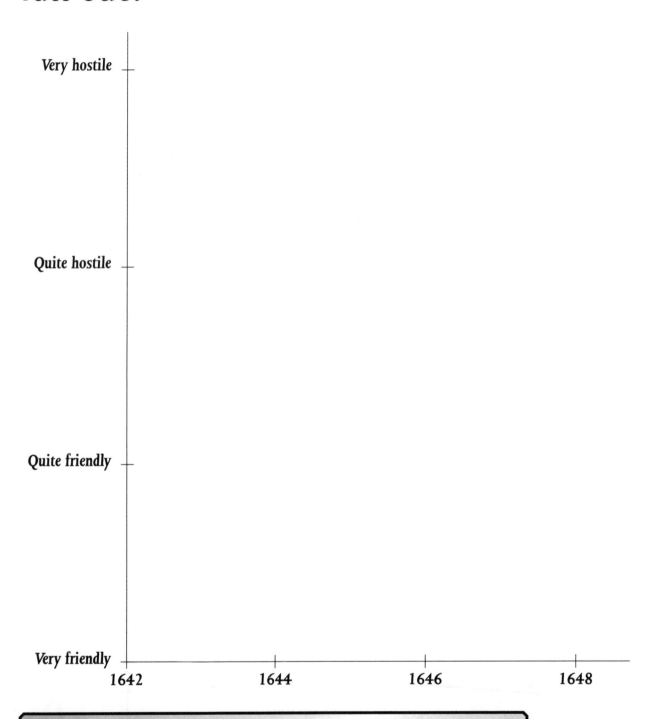

Step 1

1 Use the living graph above to show how the attitude of the King and the Scottish Parliament changed towards Parliament between 1642 and 1648. Use one colour for the King and another colour for the Scottish Parliament. You can use the information on pages 48–53 to help you.

Is the King destined for the chop?

Step 1

1 Imagine you are a Member of Parliament at the end of the Civil War. Using the information on pages 54 and 55 and what you have learnt about the Civil War, fill in the table below with what you think would be three **advantages** of executing the King and three **disadvantages** of executing the King.

Advantages of executing the King	Disadvantages of executing the King
◆	◆
◆	◆
◆	◆

Step 2

2 What do you think was the most important advantage of executing the King? Do you think executing the King was a good idea? Use the example below to help you.

The most important advantage of executing the King is _____
but the problem with this is _____

Another advantage of executing the King is _____
but, on the other hand, _____

Other points to consider include: _____
and, _____,
and _____
because _____

However, without a King, Parliament could _____

Overall I think that we should (*execute/spare) the King.   (* *Delete as appropriate*)

I think this because _____
_____
_____

The execution

Step 1

1 In the thought bubbles above write a **word** to describe the thoughts and feelings of each person as the axe was raised above Charles's head.

2 In your exercise book, or with a partner, say briefly how you would have felt if you were one of these people and had witnessed the execution.

The Execution of Charles I

Step 1

1 Below is an account of the execution of Charles I. In a red pen highlight all of the words which suggest the crowd disapproved of the execution.

2 Now imagine the crowd approved of the execution. Think of a word to replace each word you have highlighted, so that when you read the account again the crowd seem to approve of the execution.

The king stood for a moment raising his hands and eyes to Heaven and praying for silence, then slipped his cloak off and lay down with his neck on the block. The executioner bent down to make sure that his hair was not in the way, and Charles, thinking that he was preparing to strike, said, 'Stay for the sign'.

'I will, an'it please Your Majesty,' said the executioner. A fearful silence had now fallen on the little knot of people on the scaffold, on the surrounding troops, and on the crowd. Within seconds the King stretched out his hands and the executioner on the instant and at one blow severed his head from his body.

A boy of seventeen, standing a long way off in the throng, saw the axe fall. He would remember as long as he lived the sound that broke from the crowd, 'such groans as I have never heard before, and desire I may never hear again'.

Some of the guards and a few of the more determined and dextrous spectators had managed to dip handkerchiefs in the king's blood, or even to scrape up fragments of earth from below the scaffold or tear off pieces of the blood-soaked pall, but the king's body had been reverently carried back into the palace, where it was placed in a coffin and taken … to the room where it was to be embalmed.

From: *The trial of Charles I*, C. V. Wedgwood, 1964

Step 2

3 Compare the account of the execution on page 58 of your textbook with the film interpretation of Charles' execution.

4 Decide where in the triangle you would place the film account. Is it nearer to myth, fiction, or fact? Write your answer on the triangle, then compare your answer with a partner.

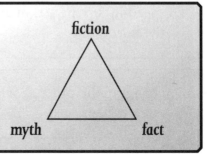

Film analysis

Step 1
1 Can you find an example from the film for each of the ways a film maker might try to increase the size of their audience and make their film more successful?

Film makers want to make money from a film by increasing the size of the audience. For a film based on real events in the past, they may do this by ...

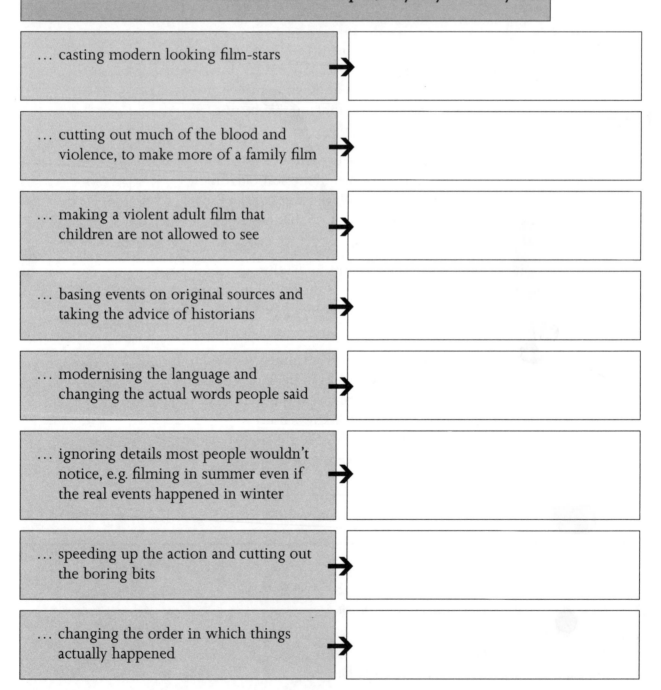

... casting modern looking film-stars →

... cutting out much of the blood and violence, to make more of a family film →

... making a violent adult film that children are not allowed to see →

... basing events on original sources and taking the advice of historians →

... modernising the language and changing the actual words people said →

... ignoring details most people wouldn't notice, e.g. filming in summer even if the real events happened in winter →

... speeding up the action and cutting out the boring bits →

... changing the order in which things actually happened →

Cromwell: 'war criminal' or just doing his job?

Step 1

1 Using what you have learnt about Cromwell, fill in the sentences below to help you answer the question: was Oliver Cromwell a 'war criminal'?

At Burford Cromwell _____
He did this because _____

At Drogheda Cromwell _____
He did this because _____

At Wexford Cromwell _____
He did this because _____

Cromwell thought he was right to do these things because _____
_____

The evidence in the 'Rules of War' suggest that Cromwell _____
_____

However, if I consider the evidence more fully my view of Cromwell as a war criminal changes. From the evidence on Burford, Cromwell in fact _____
_____

From the evidence on Drogheda I can suggest that Cromwell acted the way he did because _____
_____

From the evidence on Wexford I can suggest that Cromwell actually _____

Overall, I think that Cromwell is _____
because _____
_____

Step 2

2 Think of three questions about Cromwell's actions that you would like to have the answers to, which would help you decide if Cromwell was guilty of war crimes.

What happened after Cromwell died? (1)

Step 1

1 Imagine you are a Royalist Landowner who has lived through the reign of Charles I, the Civil War and the Restoration of Charles II.

◆ Write a letter to a friend who has gone to live in the new land of America, explaining how you feel about all the changes England has gone through. Would you think that the world was really 'turned upside down'? If so, why?

◆ To help you write your letter, look back through this section and make a chart listing all the changes. Label your chart columns 'Church', 'Government' and 'Society'. Try to use the words in the boxes below in your chart and letter.

Remember – you are a Royalist!

Church

Anglicanism/Anglican	Catholic/Catholicism
Puritan	Protestant/Protestantism
Prayerbook	

Government

Monarchy	Commonwealth
Civil War	Restoration
Divine Right of Kings	Execution
Lord Protector	Massacre
Tyrant	

Society

Trade	Great Fire of London
Theatre	The economy
Ship money	The Great Plague
Mistress	Gambling
Tax	

Presenting the Past 2 Teacher's Resources © HarperCollins *Publishers* 2002

What happened after Cromwell died? (2)

Step 1

1 Now that you have written your letter from the perspective of a Royalist Landowner, you might also like to think about how a Puritan labourer and ex-roundhead soldier would have felt about the changes.

2 Again, use the words in your chart and the boxes on the previous worksheet

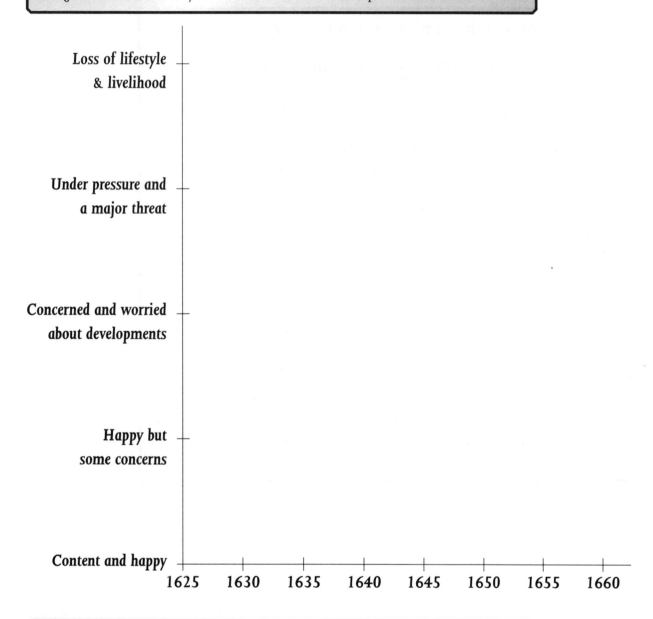

Step 2

3 Illustrate your letter with a living graph. Map how you feel about the changes which have taken place during this period and how they affect you. How have they made you feel?

Overview: the Stuart monarchy

Step 1

1 Having considered aspects of life, government and religion in the period 1625–1685, research and investigate some of the bigger questions about life in the 17th century. Use the headings in the box below to provide a framework for your investigation.

Why was the monarchy so powerful in this period?

How was Parliament's role in government changing?

Why was religion such a major cause of conflict in this period?

How did the character and personalities of Charles I and Oliver Cromwell lead to the abolition of the monarchy, and the founding of the English Republic?

Step 2

2 When investigating these key issues you might like to consider the following points:

◆ How are these issues similar or different today?

◆ What views did people have about religion, government and monarchy in the 17th century?

◆ How are peoples' views on religion, government and monarchy different today?

3 Produce a chart or diagram to illustrate the different roles played by parliament, government, monarchy and the Church in society in the 17th century compared with today.

Matching Chart: The Jacobites

This section of *Presenting the Past Book Two* (pages 68–90) relates to the QCA Scheme of Work unit 'From Glorious Revolution to the '45: how united was the kingdom?'

Presenting the Past Book Two unit title	Opportunities for Citizenship (National Curriculum for KS3)	Opportunities for Literacy (QCA *Framework*)	Key Skills	Opportunities for ICT	Thinking Skills
Who fought at the Battle of Culloden?	1a, b, d, g	7r1, 6, 8r4	C, PS, WO		
Who were the Jacobites?	1a-i	7r1, 6, 8r4	C, PS, WO		
What did the Jacobites need to be successful?	1a, b, c, f, g, h	7s8, 12, r1, 4, 6, 8, sl1, sl13, 8s12, r1, 3, 4, 5w7, 12, sl10	C, PS, WO	✔	✔
Rebellion 1: Ireland 1689–1691	1a- d, g, i	7r1, 6, 7, w11, **8**r1, 4, 5, w10	C, PS, WO		✔
Rebellion 2: Scotland 1689	1a-d, g,	7r1, 6, 7, w11, **8**r1, 4, 5, w10	C, PS, WO		✔
1691–1715: Would time help or hinder the Jacobites?	1a-d, i	7s8, 12, r1, 6, 7, w1, 11, 15, **8**s6, 12, r1, 4, 5, w1, 6, 10, 13	C, PS	✔	
Rebellion 3: Scotland and England 1715	1a-d, g, i	7r1, 6, 7, w11, **8**r1, 4, 5, w10	C, PS, WO		
1715–1745: Who needs the Stuarts?	1a-d, i	7r1, 6, 7, **8**r1, 4, 5	PS		
Rebellion 4: Scotland and England 1745–1746	1a-d, g, i	7r4, 6, 8r4	C, PS, WO		
What happened to the Jacobites?	1a- d, g	7r1, 6, 7, w1, 11, 15, 16, **8**r1, 3, 4, 5, w1, 13, 14, 16	C, PS	✔	✔
Europe in 1746	1a-d, g, i	7r1, 6, 7, **8**r1, 4, 5	C, PS, WO	✔	✔

Key:

Explanations for National Curriculum Citizenship and QCA *Framework for teaching English: Years 7, 8, and 9* abbreviations can be found on page 5 and 6 of this book.

Key Skills abbreviations: C = Communication; PS = Problem Solving; WO = Working with Others

This section develops pupil awareness of the different factors affecting the Stuart succession from the removal of James II up to the last Jacobite rebellion in 1745. Citizenship is a key underlying theme throughout. A range of rights, powers and social and moral values relevant to 17th and 18th century society are addressed, which are worthy of comparison with modern society. Pupils are made aware of how different aspects of life impacted upon all levels of society throughout what was to become the United Kingdom, by reinforcing understanding of politics and society.

The Battle of Culloden (Worksheet 3.1)

◆ This opening narrative recalls the events of the Battle of Culloden. Throughout this unit pupils will find out how the Jacobites came to be in this situation and how successful they were in their attempts to regain power.

◆ The text here is quite lengthy and you might wish to space it onto separate sheets to make it more accessible for less-able pupils. Alternatively, you might read the text aloud to the class or break the story down into smaller bite-sized chunks. Certainly, it is worth spending the time ensuring that the pupils know and understand the link between Charles I and Bonnie Prince Charlie.

◆ A descriptive writing exercise is provided on worksheet 3.1, which places particular emphasis on the story.

◆ Citizenship: there are links with democracy and power here which address the conflict between the ruling elite and those claiming the right to govern.

James and the Jacobites (w 3.2)

◆ The consequences of Culloden and the fate of James and Bonnie Prince Charlie are considered here through an investigation of the evidence. The activity looks at the origins of the dispute and the aims and objectives of the Jacobites.

◆ Worksheet 3.2 is a Stuart family tree enabling pupils to see the links between the Tudors, the Stuarts and the Jacobites.

What did the Jacobites need to be successful? (w 3.3, 3.4, 3.5)

◆ This links in with an earlier activity on Charles I, Cromwell and the English Civil War. The criteria of success are outlined on pages 72–73. Paired work enables pupils to prioritise the key issues and links in with Key Skills. Worksheet 3.3 allows low-ability pupils to access these issues.

◆ There is the opportunity for extended writing to support Literacy, through writing a letter to King James on worksheet 3.4

◆ A warm-up activity might be for small groups to identify what someone who wants to seize power needs, i.e., money, army, soldiers, weapons, support, supplies, food, ammunition, leadership, a weak enemy, luck. This could be done in the form of either a check list showing what the Jacobites did or didn't have or a chart with essential and desirable requirements.

◆ The final question identified on page 73 (what factors prevented the Jacobites from being successful?) enables pupils to move through the stepped activities which follow. Pupils are guided towards an overall judgement about how close the Jacobites really were in their attempts to remove the Hanoverians and bring about the return of the Stuarts. Worksheet 3.5 provides a chart to help pupils keep notes for this final question.

Rebellion 1: Ireland 1689–1691

◆ This section identifies the attempts in Ireland to overthrow James II, using narratives as a learning strategy.

◆ Using the success diagram on page 75 pupils can prioritise the factors and give them a score.

Rebellion 2: Scotland 1689 (w 3.6)

◆ Here pupils look at how the Scots attempted to reinstate the Stuart monarchy. The section considers the characteristics of the Scots and why they were loyal to the Stuarts and includes political, economic, social and cultural factors.

◆ The success diagram enables pupils to draw their own conclusions about the failure of the rebellion in Scotland in 1689. This activity is supported by worksheet 3.6.

◆ More-able pupils could compare the developments in Scotland with what was happening in France at the same time and the involvement of other European powers, creating an overview or bigger picture. Less-able pupils might consider fewer factors but still use the success wheel.

1691–1715: Would time help or hinder the Jacobites? (w 3.7, 3.8)

◆ It is important to reinforce pupil understanding of concepts such as help and hinder. In a discussion group pupils could consider if time would weaken William's control and increase support for James, or vice versa.

◆ Identifying political and economic factors is also important. You might look at the ways William and Mary, and later Queen Anne, attempted to consolidate their power, for instance, the Bank of England, monetary, financial and political union, and the Act of Settlement.

◆ Worksheet 3.7 deconstructs the activity at the bottom of page 79, allowing access for the less-able. More-able pupils might consider the big question and be guided through some extended writing in which they formulate a hypothesis about the Stuarts and test it against their findings in the earlier sections.

◆ Pages 80–81 identify the 'winners' and 'losers' in this dispute and there is the opportunity for pupils to do some of their own predicting, which is supported by worksheet 3.8. Pupils might also undertake an activity on the Union Jack (its origins, what/who it represents and who it doesn't), a timeline of events, a living graph charting someone's emotions during the rebellion or a venn diagram indicating strengths and weaknesses.

◆ Extension activity: following on from the summary task, the more-able might look at what historians think or what people in Scotland today think of the Act of Union. This provides the opportunity for political literacy through an investigation of devolved government in the UK today.

Rebellion 3: Scotland and England 1715

◆ Again there are eight steps looking at factors which helped and hindered the Jacobites and activities similar to the earlier sections to support pupil understanding. Extension activity: more-able pupils might look at how close the Hanoverians came to losing power.

Who needs the Stuarts?

◆ Here pupils see that the Stuarts were beginning to fall out of favour and lose the political initiative, whereas the Hanoverians consolidated their power at every turn.

◆ Pupils are prompted to bear this in mind when considering whether events from 1715 to 1745 helped or hindered the Jacobites.

Rebellion 4: Scotland and England 1745–46

◆ This section considers the significance of the Jacobites as a political force under Charles Stuart and how close they came to overthrowing the Hanoverians, culminating in the final confrontation – the Battle of Culloden.

◆ The key issue is whether, overall, events from 1715 to 1746 helped or hindered the Jacobite cause.

What happened to the Jacobites? (w 3.9)

◆ The focus of the first task is on the actions and intentions of the participants. Pupils might use a map to trace the route of the rebels and build up the story as a narrative. As they go through the narrative, they could identify some of the strengths and weaknesses of the rebels.

◆ A short role-play could help pupils to differentiate the factors and reinforce the concept of class conflict and socio-economic aspects. This could be undertaken in pairs or small groups as an extension exercise if required.

◆ Extension activity: more-able pupils could extend their understanding by using a more complex range of sources.

◆ The living graph exercise, supported by worksheet 3.9, will enable pupils to fully consider the feelings and emotions of the rebels as they headed south. A writing frame is provided to enable a piece of extended writing to be produced.

◆ You may wish to draw links with the present Royal family through a family tree to show how the throne passed from the Tudors through to the Windsors.

What was Europe like in 1746? (w 3.10)

◆ Extension activity: a map of Europe is provided (w 3.10) to enable students to identify some similarities and differences between Europe in 1558 and 1746. Some headings might be included to support the less-able or guide the investigation to look at particular issues, i.e., religion, trade, economy, ruling families.

◆ Pupils might highlight the changing political balance of power in Europe.

◆ Citizenship: you might refer to Citizenship when talking about rights and responsibilities, justice, fairness and democracy in this context and throughout this period of history. Political literacy also remains a key aspect of this final section.

The Battle of Culloden

> **Step 1**
>
> **1** In pairs, read through the first part of the story of the Battle of Culloden.

At 1.30 in the afternoon of 16th April 1746, Prince Charles Edward Stuart watched the front ranks of his Scottish Highland soldiers charge desperately towards their red-coated enemy on Culloden Moor. The Highlanders had stood their ground fiercely as they lost comrades right and left under terrible enemy fire. Some in the tightly-packed ranks had deliberately fallen to the ground to protect themselves. Others had fled in fear.

Rain and hail lashed against the Highlanders as they shouted their bloodcurdling battle cries and swept towards the enemy. Many times in the past, the redcoats had broken ranks in panic before the fierce Highland charge. Not this time.

The Highlanders became confused, caught in the thick smoke of enemy cannon. As it cleared, a line of redcoats, 30 metres away, levelled their guns and fired at the same time. Then that first rank knelt to re-load their guns, while the ranks behind fired over their heads.

The Highlanders who reached the enemy front line fought hand to hand, their swords against redcoat bayonets. Would Highland bravery be enough this time?

> **Step 2**
>
> **2** *What do you think happened next?*
> **3** *Now read the rest of the story on page 69. How does your story compare with what actually happened?*
> **4** *How close do you think the Jacobites came to winning power?*

The Stuart saga: the story so far

In 1503 Henry VIII's sister, Margaret Tudor, married James Stuart, King James IV of Scotland. Margaret and James's granddaughter was Mary Queen of Scots, who had tried to claim the throne of England when her cousin, Elizabeth Tudor was queen. When Elizabeth died without any children to inherit the throne, Mary's son, King James VI of Scotland, became king of England as well as Scotland because, being a cousin of Elizabeth, he was the next family member in line to the throne. As king of England he took the name King James I, but was also called King James VI in Scotland. James's son, Charles I was next in line to the throne. After his execution and the rule of Oliver Cromwell, Charles's son, Charles II, became King. Following Charles II's death, his brother James II took the throne.

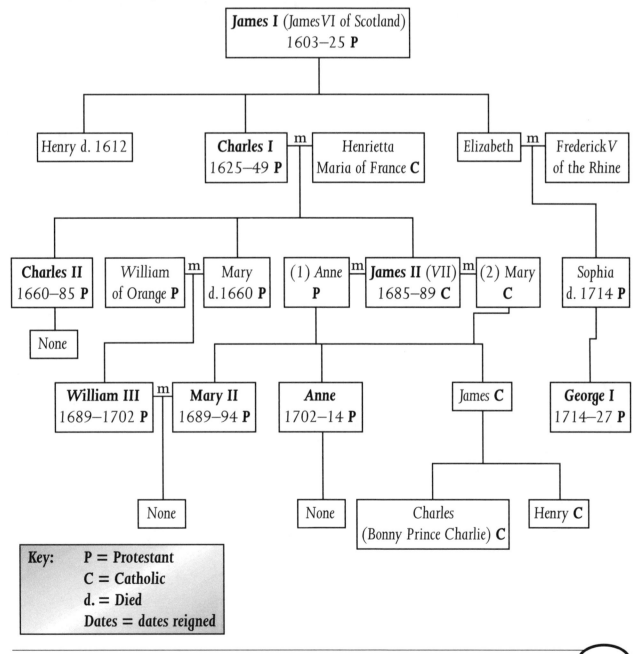

Key:
P = Protestant
C = Catholic
d. = Died
Dates = dates reigned

Six steps to success for James II

Step 1

1 Using what you have learnt about the Jacobites and the six cards on this page, decide in which order you would place the cards to help James II cross the fast-flowing river to safety and absolute power. Place each card on the appropriate step-stone. Discuss your choice with a partner and then compare your choice with another group.

| A strong army | Foreign help | Popular support |
| Good leadership | A weaker enemy | Luck |

A letter to James II

Step 1

1 Imagine you are a secret Jacobite supporter. Write a letter to King James advising him on what he needs to do to win back power. Use the information on pages 71–73 to help you outline the most important things James will need to do if he is to succeed. Remember to be polite and formal — he is your King after all!

1 April 1689

Your Royal Highness,

I am one of your most loyal and humble supporters and I am writing to suggest some ways in which you might win back power.

Firstly, may I suggest _____

_____

_____

_____

_____

_____

_____

_____

_____

_____

Extension activity

2 You could also imagine that you are a Protestant member of the English Parliament and write a letter to King William expressing your concern over the Jacobites' actions and especially the aims and ambitions of James II. Remember that you are writing to your King and to include in your answer the most important concerns you have about James's actions and the likely consequences for you and Parliament.

Success or Failure?

Step 1

1 Throughout this section you will try to answer the question: 'How close to success did the Jacobites come?' Use this chart to help you keep note of each rebellion. Colour in the appropriate square for each rebellion when deciding on a scale of 1–10 how close the Jacobites came.

2 Use the space in the first column to make notes on each rebellion. This will help you remember what happened in each attempt.

Rebellion	How close did the Jacobites come to success?		
	Nowhere near	Close	Very close
Rebellion 1: Ireland 1689–1691 ◆ ◆ ◆ ◆			
Rebellion 2: Scotland 1689 ◆ ◆ ◆ ◆			
Rebellion 3: Scotland and England 1715 ◆ ◆ ◆ ◆			
Rebellion 4: Scotland and England 1745–1746 ◆ ◆ ◆ ◆			
	1–3	4–6	7–10

Step 2

3 So, weighing up the evidence and looking at your scores, how close were the Jacobites to success in each attempt? Were any attempts more successful than others?

4 Can you think of any other factors which may have helped them achieve their aim?

 Presenting the Past 2 Teacher's Resources © HarperCollins *Publishers* 2002

Why did Scotland not support James?

Step 1

1 Fill in the table below using what you have learnt about Rebellion 2: Scotland 1689.

Highlanders were organised into clans (groups of related families), who had to obey their family chief.	So, for the Jacobites this meant …	
Highlanders were fierce and wild fighters, often feuding amongst themselves.	So, for the Jacobites this meant …	
Some clans were still Catholic, and loyal to King James.	So, for the Jacobites this meant …	
Lowland Scots hated and despised Scots from the Highlands.	So, for the Jacobites this meant …	
Highlanders thought Scots from the Lowlands were soft and weak.	So, for the Jacobites this meant …	

Step 2

2 Now read the text on page 77 and make your own chart adding any other factors which may have helped or hindered the rebellion in Scotland. For example:

John Graham of Claverhouse had no foreign support for his rebellion	So, for the Jacobites this meant …	

3 You may wish to include references to:

◆ Highland support

◆ Ambush

◆ The death of John Graham

Would time help or hinder the Jacobites?

Step 1

1 Write and illustrate a short newspaper report to explain the main events between 1691 and 1715, and whether these would help or hinder the Jacobites. Look back at your notes and decide whether to give your support to either the Jacobites or to William, Mary and Anne, write your headline in the first blank box. You might like to include a picture in the box provided. Finally, give your overall opinion.

The Chronicle

Overall

A picture of _____

Presenting the Past 2 Teacher's Resources © HarperCollins *Publishers* 2002

Scotland – a reluctant partner

Step 1

1 Look at the events described on pages 78–81. Complete the chart ticking the column which describes the effect of each event for the Jacobites.

This would **help** the Jacobites		Events	This would **hinder** the Jacobites	
A lot	A bit		A lot	A bit
		1 Bank of England	✔	
		2 Act of Settlement		
		3 English victories		
		4 Treaty of Union		

Step 2

2 For each event write a sentence or paragraph to explain how it helped or hindered the Jacobites in the table below.

	Helped or hindered	because	How/why it had this effect
Bank of England			
Act of Settlement			
English victories			
Treaty of Union			

Step 3

3 Overall, do you think events between 1691 and 1715 helped or hindered the Jacobites?

The end of the Jacobites

Step 1

1 You are going to look back at the four attempts the Jacobites made to regain power. Using your notes and what you have learnt, for each rebellion plot with a cross the number between 1 and 10 you have chosen to show how close to success the Jacobites came.

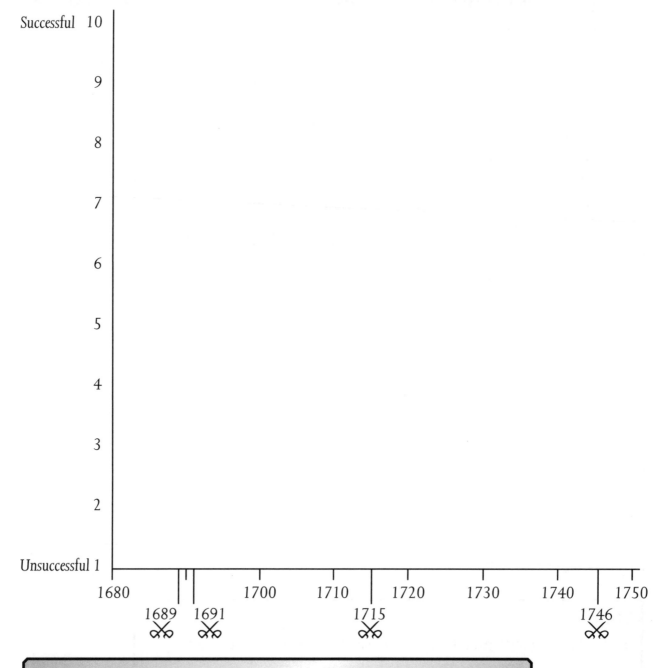

Step 2

2 Overall, how close to success do you think the Jacobites came?

Presenting the Past 2 Teacher's Resources © HarperCollins *Publishers* 2002

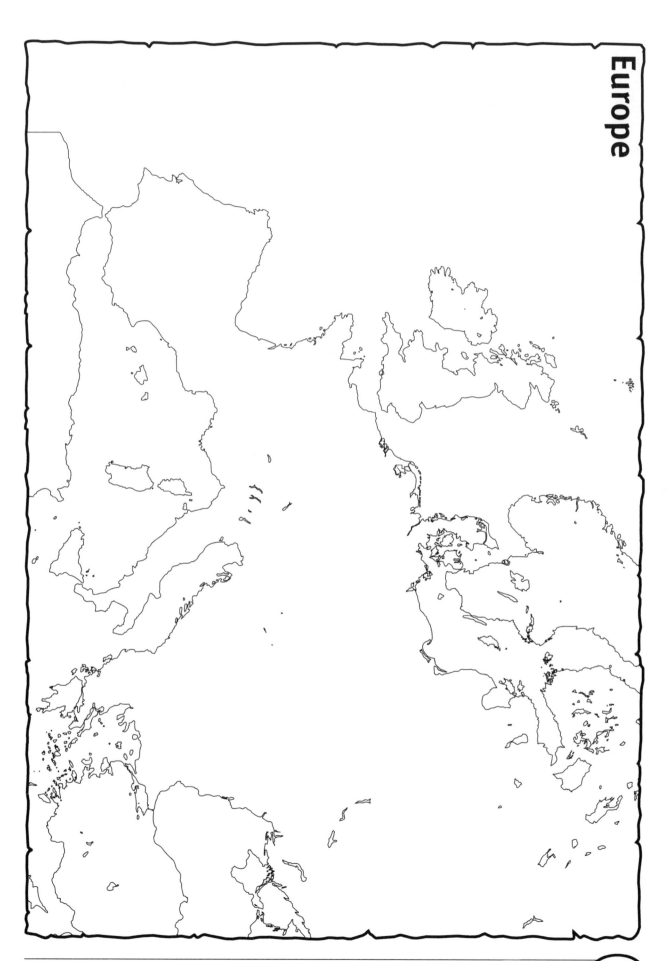

Europe

Matching Chart: Images of an Age

This section of *Presenting the Past Book Two* (pages 91–109) relates to the QCA Scheme of Work unit 'Images of an age: what can we learn from portraits 1500–1750?'

Presenting the Past Book Two unit title	Opportunities for Citizenship (National Curriculum for KS3)	Opportunities for Literacy (QCA *Framework*)	Key Skills	Opportunities for ICT	Thinking Skills
Images of an age: what can portraits tell us about Elizabeth I?	1a, d, h,	7r1, 6, 10, w1, **8**r4, 8, w1, 6, 7	C, PS, WO	✔	
Elizabeth in later life	1a, d, h	7r1, 6, 10, w1, **8**r4, 10, w1, 6, 7	PS, WO	✔	✔
What do portraits not tell us about Elizabeth?	1a, d, h	7r1, 6, 8, 10, **8**r4, 6, 8	C, PS, WO	✔	✔
Can we use modern film as historical evidence?	1a, b, d, h	7r1, 6, 8, 10,w5, **8**r4, 6, 8, w6, 8	C, PS, WO	✔	
Images of whose age? Exhibition 1: Macaulay's Country 1500–1750	1a, b, c, h	7r1, 6, 10, w11, 15, **8**r4, 8, w10	C, PS, WO	✔	
The picture gallery	1a, b, c, d, h	7r2, 6, 8, 10, **8**r4, 5, 6, 8	C, PS, WO	✔	✔
Exhibition 2: Davies's Country 1500–1750	1a, b, c, d, h	7r1, 6, 10, w11, 15, 16 **8**r4, 8, w10, 13, 14	C, PS, WO	✔	

Key:

Explanations for National Curriculum Citizenship and QCA *Framework for teaching English: Years 7, 8, and 9* abbreviations can be found on page 5 and 6 of this book.

Key Skills abbreviations: C = Communication; PS = Problem Solving; WO = Working with Others

The focus of this section is to look at historical interpretations and representations of the period 1500–1750. Pupils are encouraged to analyse and interpret different portraits of Elizabeth and other historical figures, evaluating them as evidence. They will consider the significance of portraits, assessing the purpose and function of portraits and images across time, with a focus on propaganda. Students are encouraged to develop higher-level thinking skills by evaluating sources, interpreting key features and drawing conclusions from a visual source. Throughout this last unit there are elements of Citizenship, Thinking Skills and Literacy. The overall aim is to enable pupils to evaluate both the historical value of portraits and visual evidence, as well as what they tell us about the figure/event in question.

What can portraits tell us about Elizabeth I?

◆ Pupils examine and analyse a portrait of Elizabeth, drawing conclusions about how and why she controlled images of herself.

◆ Pupils might also write about what they would include in a portrait of themselves. How might they want to be presented? This would promote analysis and interpretation and an awareness of Elizabeth's thinking.

Elizabeth in later life (Worksheet 4.1)

◆ Pupils begin to compare different images. The tasks prompt pupils to consider the bigger question – are portraits useful to historians?

◆ Pupils could examine how politicians or famous people use portraits today. Using worksheet 4.1 pupils can analyse their chosen person and decide what they can see in the pictures, for example images of wealth, power, health, fashion, taste/style. Breaking down the activity into smaller chunks might also be a useful exercise.

◆ You could set up a Mind Mapping exercise. Groups of four people look at the portrait for 20 seconds in turn, and draw the part of the picture they looked at. They should look at Elizabeth's clothing, jewellery, and background features as well as her face. The group construct their own portrait of Elizabeth based on the little bit of the picture they each saw. Groups compare their version with others and the portrait to see how accurate they were.

What do portraits not tell us? (w 4.2, 4.3)

◆ As a warm-up activity the class might undertake some brainstorming about the 'problem' with portraits. (Worksheet 4.2).

◆ Any models of Elizabeth or Elizabethan artefacts/objects would be very useful here. Pupils will use VAK accelerated learning strategies to identify how they would make a person feel. Pupils could even make their own Elizabethan artefacts.

◆ A role-play might concern what Elizabeth could have been thinking as she sat having her portrait done. Different portraits of Elizabeth would provide differentiated activities.

◆ Pupils could work in groups of three to undertake the tasks on page 99 with a different portrait each. Pupils investigate the portraits in a detailed and individual way. Worksheet 4.3 enables pupils to decide which portrait of Elizabeth is the most realistic, considering what they have learnt about propaganda and portraits.

Can we use modern films as historical evidence? (w 4.4)

◆ Pupils are brought up-to-date with modern film interpretations. Hollywood-style postcards of stills from films might be used as further examples (e.g. Glenda Jackson's, *Elizabeth R*).

◆ Pupils consider how and why film versions of famous people and historical events are often not accurate and have been altered, considering images of Elizabeth at different points in her life and in different contexts. Pupils create their own storyboard using worksheet 4.4. Less-able students may need to be provided with a template.

◆ You might broaden out the activity or a discussion to look at other historical figures and events as represented in film. Examples might be Raleigh, Drake or Guy Fawkes. You could use films such as *Robin Hood: Prince of Thieves*, *Braveheart*, and *The Patriot*.

Images of whose age? Exhibition 1

◆ There is a strong link with propaganda in this section. For higher level pupils you may wish to introduce the idea of propaganda and the use of portraits as a political tool, i.e., presenting a particular image of a religious group. The activity includes references to leaders from Henry VIII to George II – all with their own individual characteristics, values and beliefs. This section will need to be further differentiated to support less-able pupils.

The picture gallery (w 4.5)

◆ The images contain a variety of social, political and religious images, which pupils can analyse and interpret accordingly (Worksheet 4.5). These may be used as a smaller set.

Exhibition 2

◆ Here pupils learn that visual images can be used to support different hypotheses. This particular interpretation is based upon class and social status. Pupils also consider the images from a modern perspective rather than a 19th century view.

◆ Less-able pupils may need fewer pictures and a re-structured activity to enable them to access the higher level skills. More-able pupils might build upon Exhibition 1 and construct their own exhibition of images of life in the 21st century. Extension activity: the whole class construct an exhibition of life in the 21st century, looking at different perspectives/aspects. Pupils research their own exhibits of Elizabethan life using museum and gallery websites and the virtual reality tours various museums have on their websites, to 'acquire' objects/artefacts.

A portrait of my favourite famous person

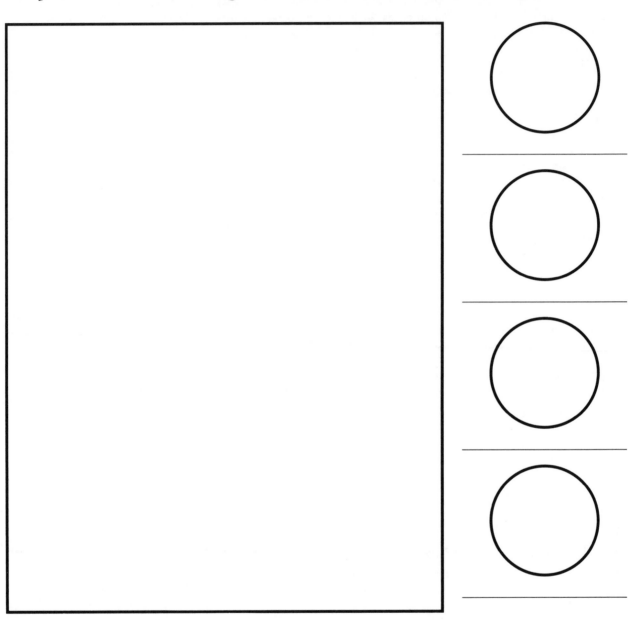

Step 1

1 *Choose a photograph or picture of your favourite person. Cut it out from a magazine and place it onto the square above.*

2 *Choose four important parts of the picture and draw them into the empty bubbles.*

3 *Describe briefly what is in each bubble.*

4 *What do the objects you have chosen tell us about:*

◆ why this person is famous

◆ what this person wants people to know about them

◆ what objects they might not want included in the picture/photograph?

The problem with portraits is …

Step 1

1 Fill in the writing frame below to help you decide whether portraits are useful to historians as evidence.

A portrait can be useful because:

◆ _____
◆ _____
◆ _____
◆ _____

But a portrait can also be a problem because:

◆ _____
◆ _____
◆ _____
◆ _____

When I have my school photograph taken

◆ I like it because _____

◆ I don't like it because _____

Extension Activity

2 Fill in the writing frame below to help you decide whether films are useful to historians as evidence.

◆ So, if I had gained all of my information about Elizabeth from a film and no other evidence, I would describe Elizabeth's character as _____

◆ I would describe her appearance as _____

◆ I would describe the early events in her reign as _____

◆ I would think she treated Catholics _____

◆ This would/would* not be supported by the historical evidence we have about Elizabeth because _____

(*delete as appropriate)

Spot the difference!

Step 1

1 Look through the pictures on pages 96–97, is there anything the same about Elizabeth in each picture? Is there anything different? Cut out the cards below and place them on the chart under the heading you think is the most appropriate, e.g., *Elizabeth's jewellery is similar in each picture.*

Similar	Different

Facial Expression	Clothes
Hair	Position/pose/posture
Eyes	Symbols
Complexion	Jewellery

Step 2

2 Look at the two columns in your chart. What do they tell you about portraits? Do you think portraits can be trusted as historical evidence?

My film

Step 1

1 Use this storyboard and what you have learnt about Elizabeth I to help you plan a modern film about Elizabeth. Your film must be critical and negative about her. It must favour the Catholics of the time and Elizabeth's other enemies. It must be an exciting thriller about hatred and power.

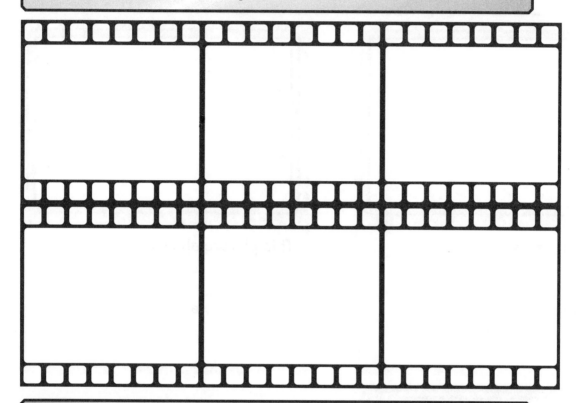

Step 2

2 First, choose a title. Then look back at what you have learnt about Elizabeth. You will find the sections on the Church, Catholics and Protestants and the Armada important.

3 Choose six scenes. Draw each scene and write about it. Decide the kind of costume you would use and some dialogue too.

Extension Activity

This section has looked at film representations of Elizabeth. You could, using the same technique, look at film interpretations of other key historical figures. You could apply the same approach when looking at Robin Hood, Guy Fawkes or even William Wallace. You might consider looking at two important Elizabethan figures. Sir Francis Drake, William Shakespeare, and Sir Walter Raleigh have all appeared as characters in film. See how modern films have interpreted their role and importance in history compared to historians' views of their achievements.

A Portrait Gallery

Step 1

1 Choose any three portraits and sketch them in the boxes below. For each one identify objects, symbols or aspects of the portrait which represent the following themes:

- ◆ Power and the right to rule
- ◆ Authority and government
- ◆ Religion and upholding the faith
- ◆ Justice and law

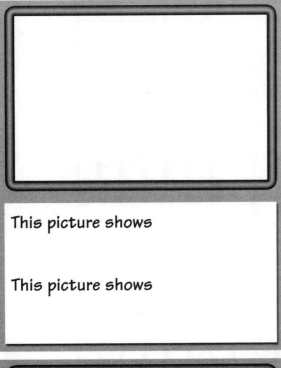

This picture shows

This picture shows

This picture shows

This picture shows

This picture shows

This picture shows

Step 2

2 When identifying these themes, as well as looking for actual objects try to consider the expression, posture and pose of the person in the portrait. For example, is the figure standing still, active, riding a horse, hunting or worshipping?

Remember, the purpose of this activity is to enable you to analyse and interpret a variety of portraits and consider the key historical concepts of motive, purpose and audience when analysing any historical source.

Presenting the Past 2 Teacher's Resources © HarperCollins *Publishers* 2002